THE
WONDER
OF
HANDS

THE
WONDER
OF
HANDS

written by *Edith Baer*

photographs by *Tana Hoban*

Parents' Magazine Press

New York.

Hands can do all kinds of things . . .

Change a tire   bake a pie

Fly a kite or catch a fly

Plant a seed and help it grow

Point the way for feet to go.

Hands can feel and hands can heal

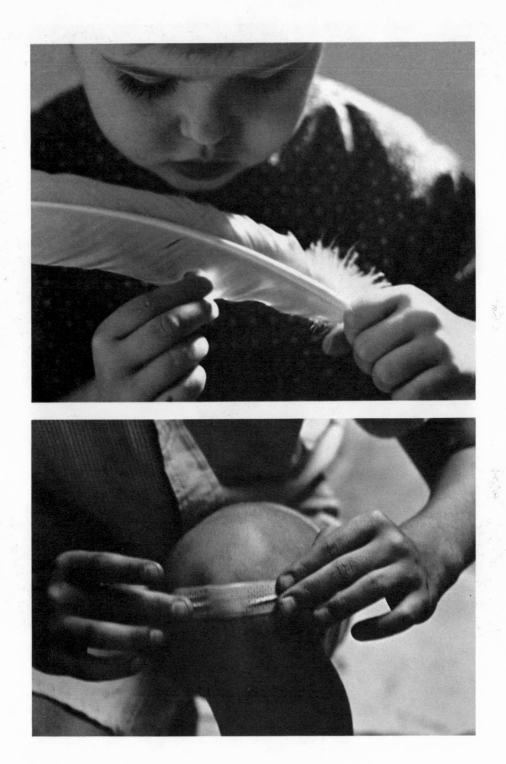

Work in clay or work with steel

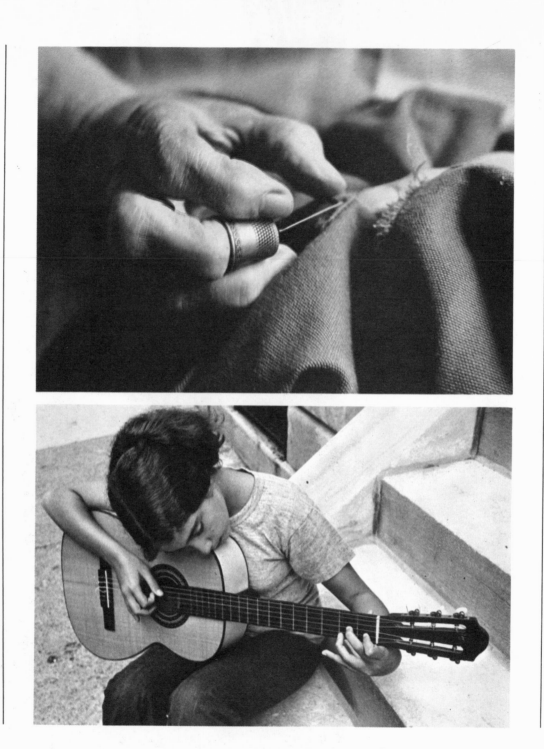

Patch a pocket, play a song

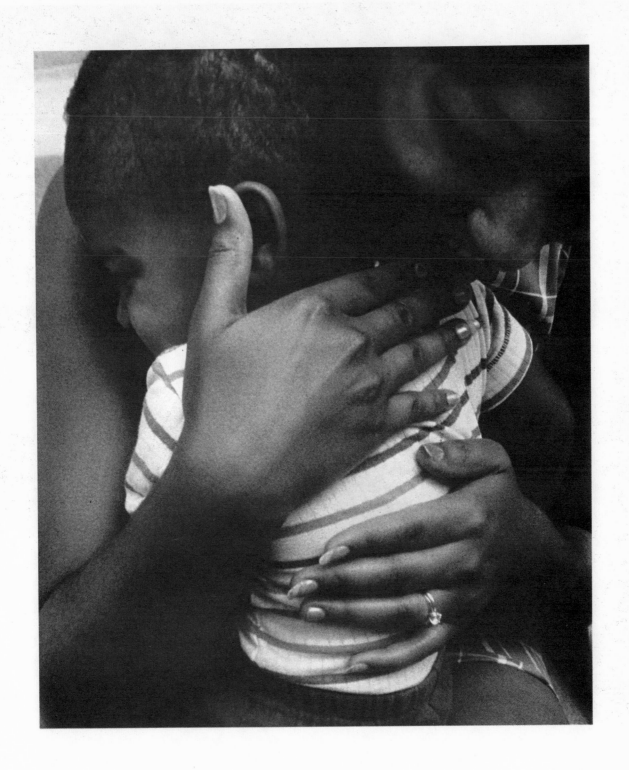

Soothe a hurt and right a wrong.

Hands can make all kinds of things . . .

Big and strong and sturdy things

Fragile things, frilly things
Even downright silly things!

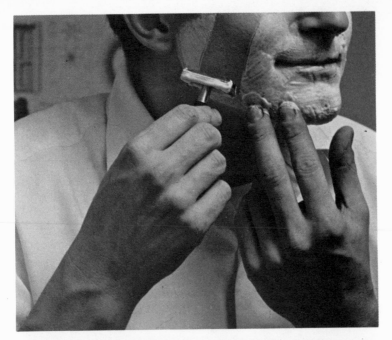

Hands shave beards and tie a tie

Blow a kiss and wave good-bye

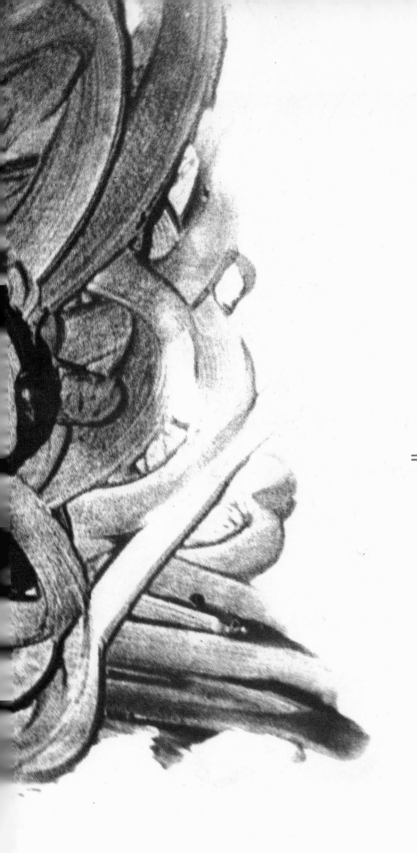

Finger-paint

Try on a hat
Train a puppy, stroke a cat.

Hands do many different things . . .
Clap for joy, flap like wings

Move a crane, dig a moat
Build a boat and let it float!

Hands begin where others end
Form a circle, find a friend

Fix a toy, stop a fight

Tuck you into bed at night.

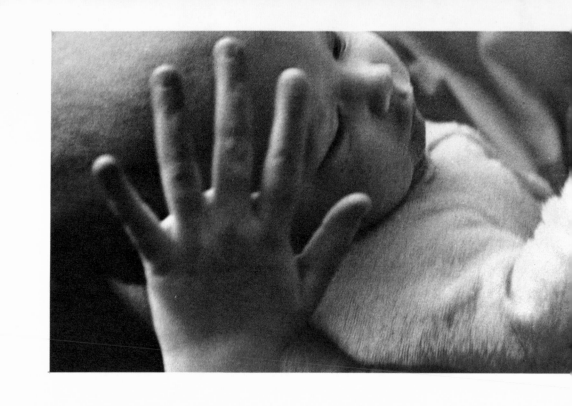

Hands can touch
and hands can teach.

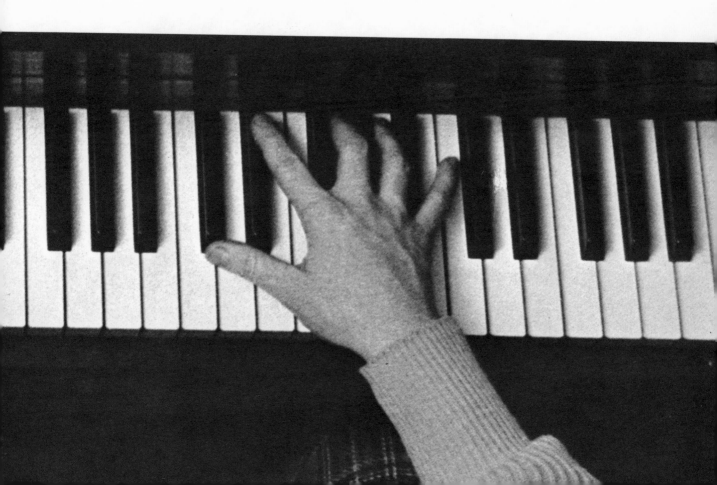

Hands can hold

and fold

and reach.

Rough hands, smooth hands
Plump hands, thin
Hands like wrinkled apple skin.

Hands can do most anything . . .
Wear a ring   wear a glove

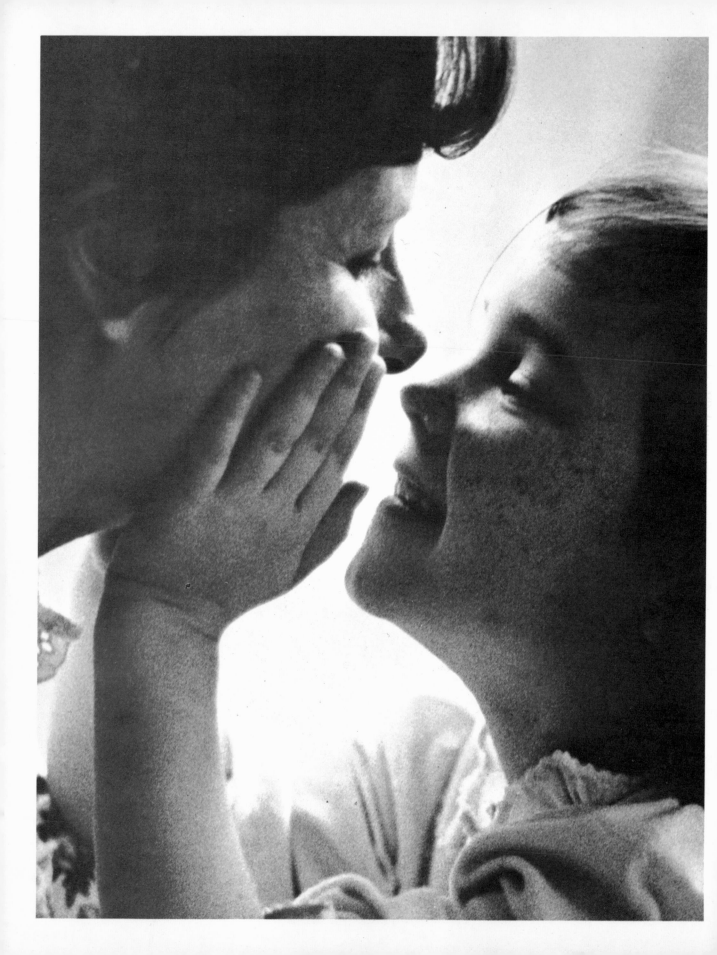